A Fresh Approach
to Piano Sight-Reading

Joining
the Dots

Book 4

Alan Bullard

ABRSM

To the Teacher

Joining the Dots offers lots of material to help build your pupil's skill and confidence in sight-reading. Used as part of regular lessons and practice, it will help students learn to read new music more quickly and easily, developing their awareness of keyboard geography, their sense of key and other general musicianship skills.

The five books in the series cover the keys found in ABRSM's sight-reading tests at each of Grades 1–5, with a section for each key.

In Book 4, each section begins with warm-up and technical material ('Workouts'), followed by opportunities for improvisation ('Make Music') and several short pieces to sight-read ('Read and Play'). Unlike the other books in the series, there are no 'Key Features' in this book, because no new keys are introduced.

Workouts are for exercising and warming up the fingers and hands in the key, and explore a range of techniques. The first of each pair is the same throughout (transposed for each key), to help reinforce key familiarity, while the second is always different.

Make Music provides an opportunity for your pupil to build confidence in (and through) creative and imaginative work, encouraging familiarity with the 'feel' of the key using an approach that is not primarily notation-based. In this book, pupils can create a short piece either by continuing a two-bar opening or by adding a lower or upper part to a given part. The ideas here can be used in a flexible way, and the approach and strategy you adopt will probably vary for each student. Encourage your pupil to be as inventive as possible while keeping the features of the chosen key in mind.

Read and Play is the goal of each section – a number of short, characterful pieces, to be played at sight or after a short practice time, with the focus on keeping going. These lead up to and include the technical standard to be found in Grade 4 sight-reading and are a useful source of sight-reading material for those preparing for exams.

Because the material is arranged to be at an equivalent level in each key, your pupil can 'jump in' to any section, using it alongside pieces, scales or arpeggios that are being learnt in that key. Within each section, the books are designed so that pupils learn and play the Workouts before moving on to the Make Music and Read and Play material. The suggested fingerings should work for most players, but are a recommendation only.

Towards the end of the book you will find **More Pieces to Play**, including longer solo pieces and a duet. These can be used in any way you wish – as additional sight-reading practice or as pieces to learn quickly and play through for fun.

with thanks to Janet for her sound advice,
and to her pupils for trying these ideas out

First published in 2010 by ABRSM (Publishing) Ltd, a wholly owned subsidiary of ABRSM
24 Portland Place, London W1B 1LU, United Kingdom

© 2010 by The Associated Board of the Royal Schools of Music

AB 3424

Illustrations by Willie Ryan, www.illustrationweb.com/willieryan
Book design and cover by www.adamhaystudio.com
Music and text origination by Barnes Music Engraving Ltd
Printed in England by Halstan & Co. Ltd, Amersham, Bucks.

Dear Pianist,

Joining the Dots will help you to learn new music more quickly and easily.

In this book you will find a section for each key that you are likely to use.

	page		page
C major	4	D major	22
A minor	7	B minor	25
G major	10	Bb major	28
E minor	13	G minor	31
F major	16	A major	34
D minor	19	Eb major	37

In each section there are several different things to do:

Workouts to exercise your fingers and hands

Read and Play where there are a number of short pieces to play – read the title, work out the rhythm, find the notes and, when you're ready, play the piece right through without stopping!

Make Music in which you can develop and explore musical ideas

Towards the end of the book you'll find **More Pieces to Play**, including some longer pieces and a duet for you to play with a friend.

Enjoy Joining the Dots!

Alan Bullard

C major

Workouts

• Use these to warm up in the key of C major

Flowing but rhythmic

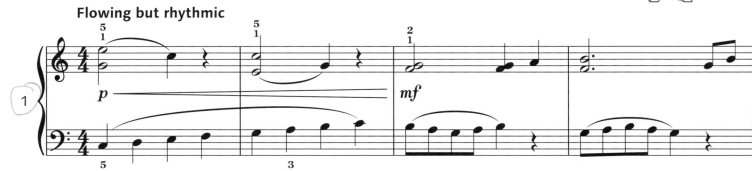

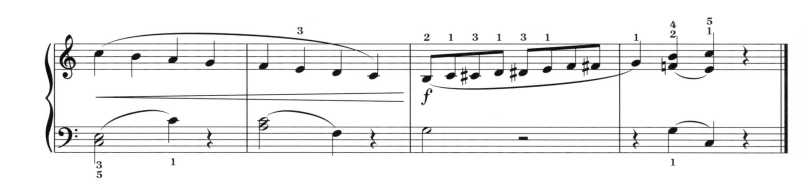

Allegretto

Make Music
Hop, Skip and Jump

- Make up a piece in the key of C major, starting as shown
- Aim for about 8 bars in total

- You could repeat the musical ideas at different pitches
- Think about where the 'hop, skip and jump' might be in your piece
- Consider contrasts in dynamics and articulation

Read and Play

- Prepare carefully, looking out for changes in hand position
- If you like, take a moment to try out the piece
- Finally, play it right through without stopping

Poem

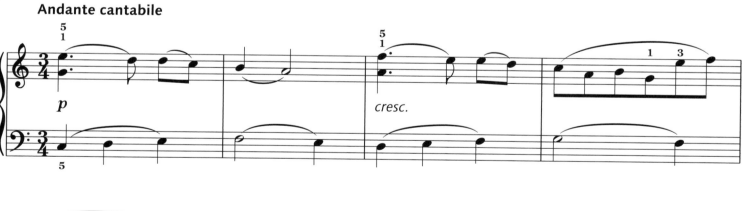

C major

Country Dance

Black Beetle and Greenfly

Workouts

- Use these to warm up in the key of A minor

Flowing but rhythmic

- Pass the left hand over the right hand for each clef change

Allegretto

A minor

Make Music
Pacing Round and Round

- Make up a piece in the key of A minor by adding your own continuation of the right-hand melody
- You might like to imagine an animal pacing around a cage
- Think about how the dynamics might change throughout your piece

Read and Play

- Prepare carefully, looking out for changes in hand position
- If you like, take a moment to try out the piece
- Finally, play it right through without stopping

Two Mice

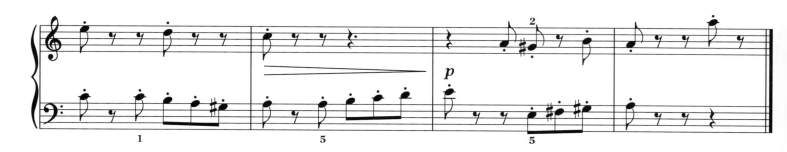

8

Sarabande for J.S.B.

A Minor Incident

G major

Workouts

- Use these to warm up in the key of G major

Flowing but rhythmic

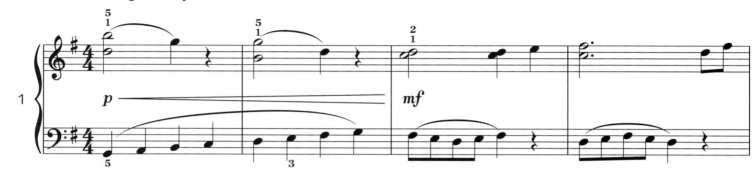

Tempo di valse

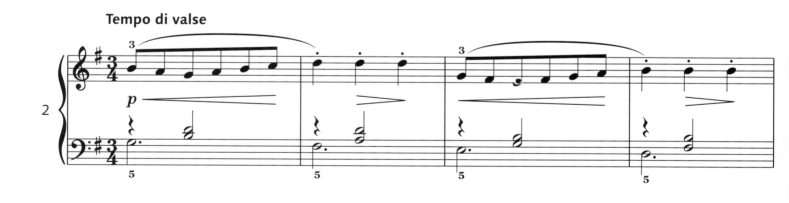

Make Music
Phone a Friend!

- Make up a piece in the key of G major, starting as shown
- Aim for about 8 bars in total

- Imagine a lively conversation, in which there's so much to say that the sentences never get finished!
- You could try turning bar 1 upside down or repeating the ideas at different pitches

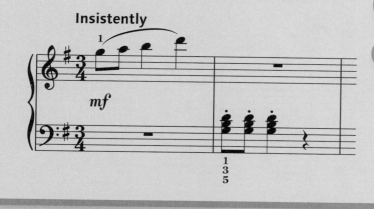

Read and Play

- Prepare carefully, looking out for changes in hand position
- If you like, take a moment to try out the piece
- Finally, play it right through without stopping

Tidying Up!

Chitter-Chatter

Allegretto leggiero

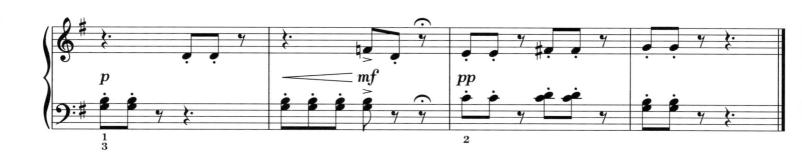

A Stately Occasion

Tempo di minuetto

Workouts

• Use these to warm up in the key of E minor

Flowing but rhythmic

Allegretto (quavers may be swung ♫ = ♩♪)

Make Music
Gathering Clouds

- Make up a piece in the key of E minor by adding your own continuation of the left-hand melody
- Consider varying the dynamics as the piece moves along
- You might like to slow down near the end

Andante espressivo

Read and Play

- Prepare carefully, looking out for changes in hand position
- If you like, take a moment to try out the piece
- Finally, play it right through without stopping

Interrupted Conversation

Lively

Call of the Homeland

Andante

Waking Up

Allegretto

F major

Workouts

- Use these to warm up in the key of F major

Flowing but rhythmic

1

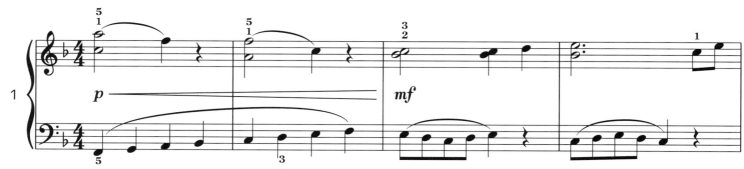

With a steady beat

2

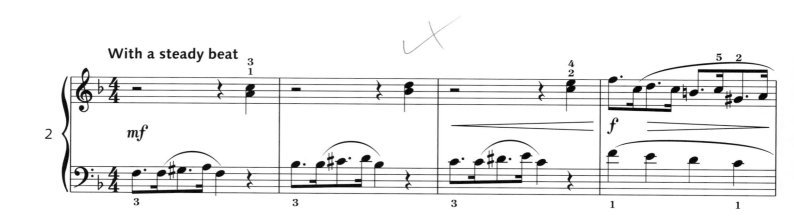

Make Music
Village Fair

- Make up a piece in the key of F major, starting as shown
- Aim for about 8 bars in total

- Try repeating the right-hand rhythms using different pitches
- You might like to keep the left hand the same throughout

Read and Play

- Prepare carefully, looking out for changes in hand position
- If you like, take a moment to try out the piece
- Finally, play it right through without stopping

Aria

Carnival Chorus

With rhythmic confidence

Two Snakes

D minor

Workouts

- Use these to warm up in the key of D minor

Flowing but rhythmic

1

Moderato grazioso

2

Make Music
Flat Feet

- Make up a piece in the key of D minor, starting as shown
- Aim for about 8 bars in total

- Try turning the right-hand idea upside down
- You could continue to use the hands separately (until the last bar, perhaps)

Alla marcia

Read and Play

- Prepare carefully, looking out for changes in hand position
- If you like, take a moment to try out the piece
- Finally, play it right through without stopping

Open Spaces

Andante

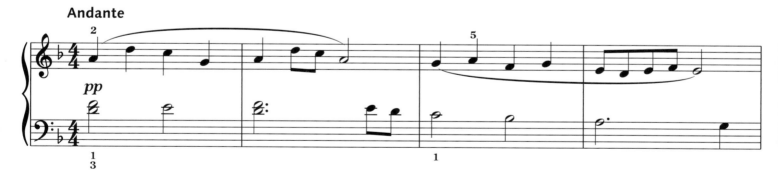

The Haunted Forest

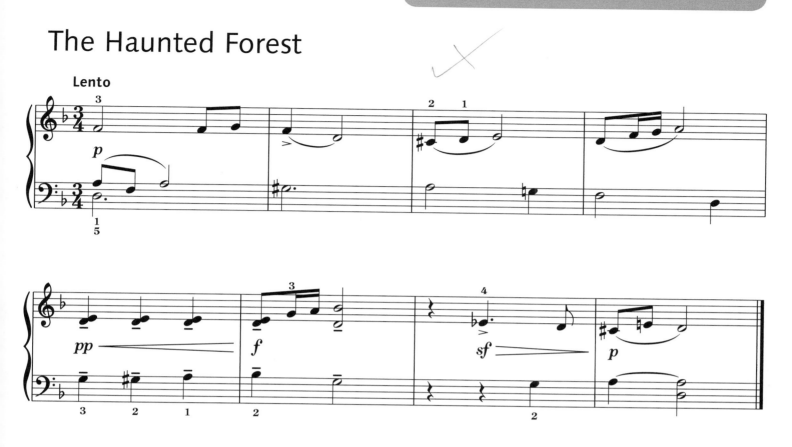

On your Bike!

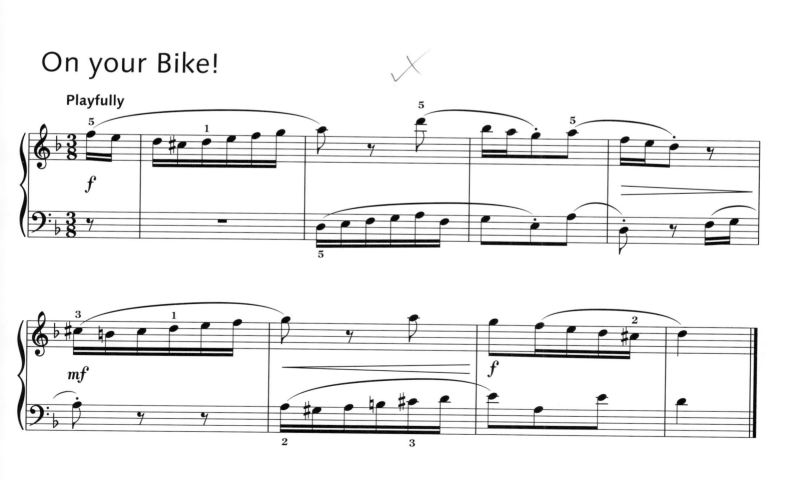

D major

Workouts

• Use these to warm up in the key of D major

Flowing but rhythmic

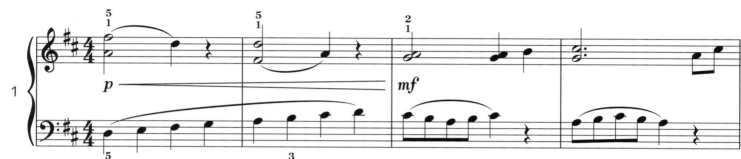

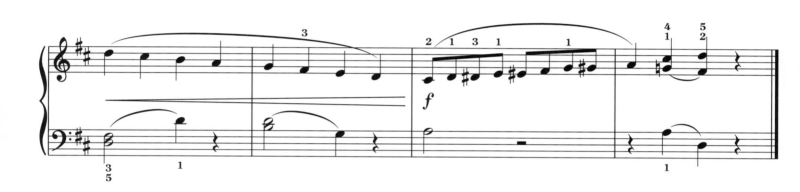

Adagio cantabile

Make Music

Ducks on the Lake

- Make up a piece in the key of D major by adding your own continuation of the right-hand melody
- Aim to create a picture of the bobbing and quacking ducks
- Think about how you could use contrasts in dynamics and articulation

Moderate speed, with humour

Read and Play

- Prepare carefully, looking out for changes in hand position
- If you like, take a moment to try out the piece
- Finally, play it right through without stopping

Reflections

Andante

D major

Bandstand

Come Skate with Me

Workouts

- Use these to warm up in the key of B minor

Flowing but rhythmic

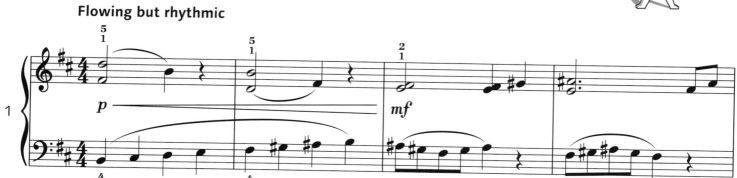

Andante cantabile

Make Music

Melting Snow

- Make up a piece in the key of B minor by filling in the gaps in the right-hand melody
- To begin with, try repeating the rhythms of the first two bars
- The final bars could die away to nothing, using fewer notes, as suggested

Read and Play

- Prepare carefully, looking out for changes in hand position
- If you like, take a moment to try out the piece
- Finally, play it right through without stopping

A Long Walk Home

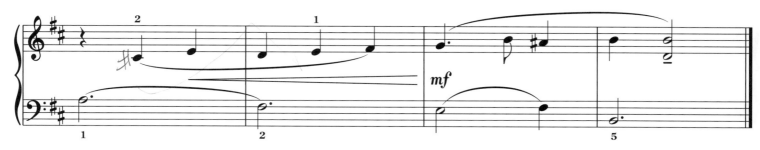

26

Sprint to the Finish

Fast and rhythmic

Cavalcade

Alla marcia

B♭ major

Workouts

• Use these to warm up in the key of B♭ major

Flowing but rhythmic

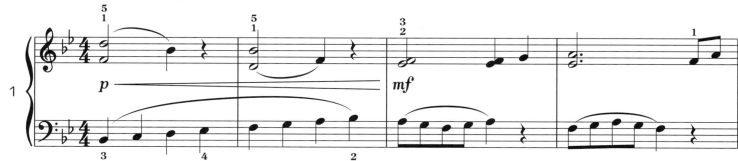

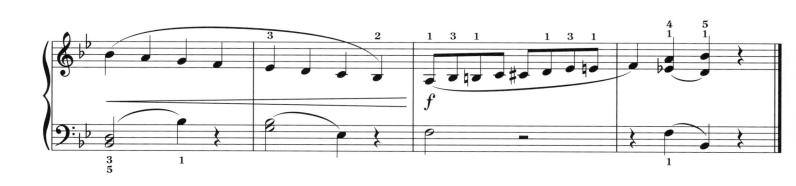

Allegretto

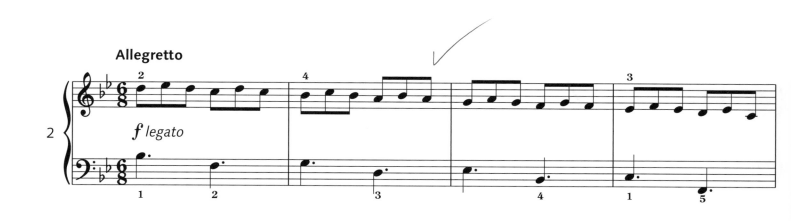

Make Music
Brass Band

- Make up a piece in the key of Bb major by filling in the gaps in the right-hand part
- Aim for a full and confident sound throughout
- Try to continue the rhythmic character of the opening in your melody

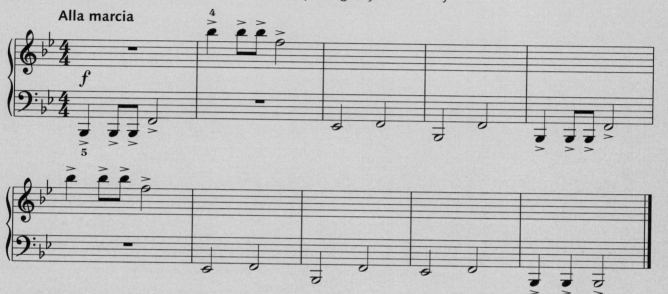

Read and Play

- Prepare carefully, looking out for changes in hand position
- If you like, take a moment to try out the piece
- Finally, play it right through without stopping

Ambling Anthony

The Chimes Waltz

With ringing tone

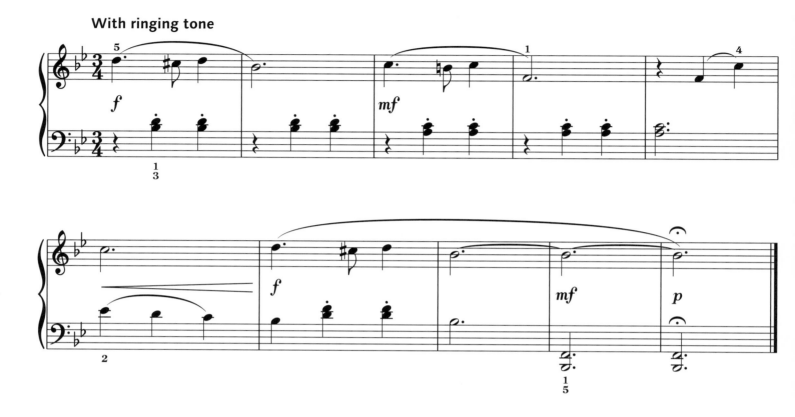

Summer's Morning

Allegretto giocoso

Workouts

- Use these to warm up in the key of G minor

Flowing but rhythmic

Allegro vivo

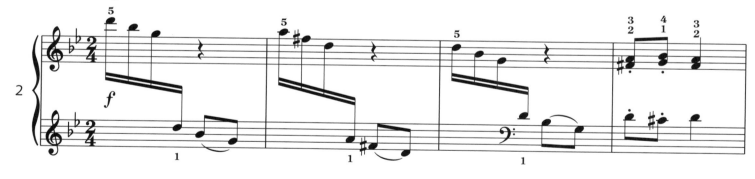

Make Music
Here and There

- Make up a piece in the key of G minor, starting as shown
- Aim for about 8 bars in total

- Try using the two musical ideas at different pitches
- You could turn the left-hand idea upside down
- Think about using contrasts in dynamics to communicate the mood

Quite fast and scurrying

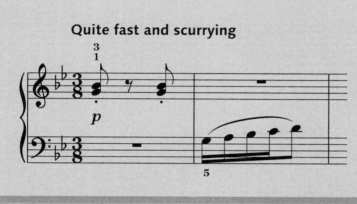

Read and Play

- Prepare carefully, looking out for changes in hand position
- If you like, take a moment to try out the piece
- Finally, play it right through without stopping

Lively Conversation

Allegretto

Tango for Two

Slow but rhythmic

Past Regrets

Andante mesto

A major

Workouts

- Use these to warm up in the key of A major

Flowing but rhythmic

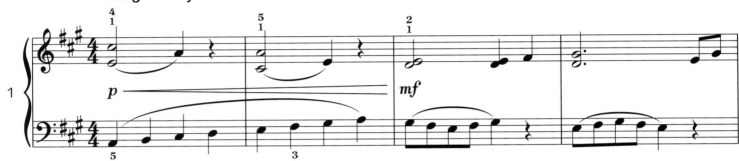

Andantino grazioso

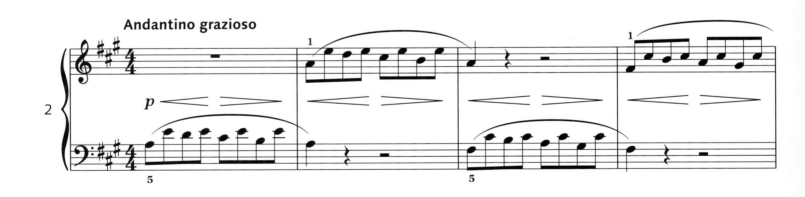

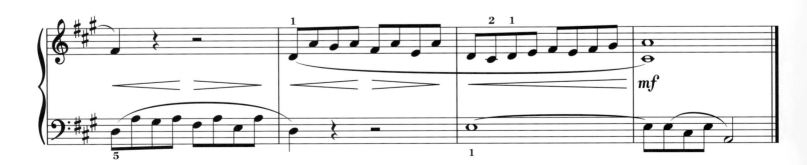

Make Music

Relaxing in the Sun

- Make up a piece in the key of A major by adding your own continuation of the right-hand melody
- Add your own expression marks
- Notice the pauses in the second line – you can take a little time to relax here!

Andante

Read and Play

- Prepare carefully, looking out for changes in hand position
- If you like, take a moment to try out the piece
- Finally, play it right through without stopping

Lullaby

Gently and calmly

A major

Pausing for Thought

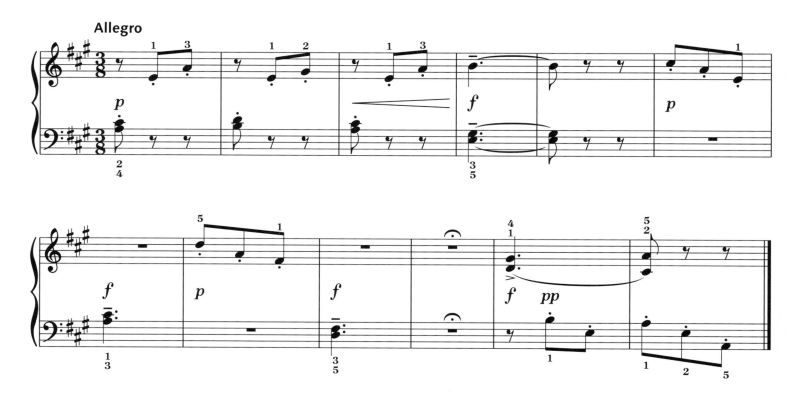

Duck and Drake

E♭ major

Workouts

- Use these to warm up in the key of E♭ major

Flowing but rhythmic

1

Vivace

2

Make Music
Antique Dance

- Make up a piece in the key of E♭ major by adding your own continuation of the right-hand melody
- Try using the opening musical shape at different pitches, perhaps by moving downwards in parallel with the left hand

Read and Play

- Prepare carefully, looking out for changes in hand position
- If you like, take a moment to try out the piece
- Finally, play it right through without stopping

Springtime

38

More Pieces to Play

- On the remaining pages you will find a variety of pieces of different lengths
- You can use these for playing at sight, or as pieces to learn on your own or with your teacher
- Don't forget to check the key signature and look out for changes in hand position

Shopping Mall Blues

At a moderate speed

Wizards and Witches

Allegretto

Fireside

Jumping Fish

Underground Train

With a steady rock beat

Dog Chasing its Tail

Scherzando

Forest Fanfares

Gentle and calm

Hoedown

Tender Attraction

Moderato cantabile

• Here's a duet to play with a friend

Clog Dance

Clog Dance

Fancy Dress Ball

D.C. al Fine

06/14